Human cloning
- right or wrong?

Dr Eryl Davies

EVANGELICAL PRESS

EVANGELICAL PRESS
Faverdale North Industrial Estate, Darlington, DL3 0PH, England

Evangelical Press USA
P. O. Box 825, Webster, New York 14580, USA

e-mail: sales@evangelicalpress.org

web: www.evangelicalpress.org

First published 2003

British Library Cataloguing in Publication Data available

ISBN 0 85234 551 8

Printed and bound in Great Britain by Aztec Colour Print, Washington, Tyne & Wear.

Contents

1.
Science fiction

Has science fiction now come true? That is what some people believe about cloning. Think, for example, of the science fiction film *The 6th Day,* which attempts to portray American society in the future.

One of the adult characters in the film, called Adam, returns home from work one evening only to discover that he had been cloned. It was a real lookalike. And the clone had also been given all of Adam's memories.

The clone in this film was the creation of a dubious business company specializing in secret, illegal cloning. But this was no ordinary commercial enterprise. The proprietor of the cloning company, as well as his clients, saw beyond the financial dimensions of cloning. Their ultimate aim was to search for ways of living on earth eternally. The film posed the possibility of providing a scientific answer for people who want to go on living physically on earth for ever.

A simple answer was proposed in the film. As individuals grew older or found that their lives were restricted or even threatened by disease, they were invited to become cloned and, at the same time, have all their memories transferred to a new cloned body.

Now that is science fiction. Or, is it now a fact in the twenty-first century? Some think it is, so read on.

2.
Fact or fiction?

One contemporary example of people who believe that reproductive cloning is now a reality, not fiction, is the Raelian sect. This was founded in France in 1973 by a journalist, Claude Vorilhon, who is now usually referred to as Raël. Active in eighty-four countries, the sect claims over 60,000 members and a growing international appeal.

How is the sect linked to cloning? One link is that Raël believes that extra-terrestrial beings with a superb mastery of genetic engineering actually created humans. This is, of course, pure fantasy. However, Raël elaborates this fantasy in a bizarre and blasphemous way; but more of that later. So why cloning? Because Raël teaches that the human soul dies when physical death occurs, the key to eternal life on earth is not spiritual but scientific. For Raël, the scientific answer lies in the recreation of individuals from their own DNA; in other words, cloning.

Another link between Raelianism and cloning is more daring. Raël is reported to have joined with several other investors to establish 'the first company in the world to offer a human cloning service'.[1] The company was registered as Valiant Ventures Ltd but is widely known, and advertised, as Clonaid. Raël's company was formed immediately after the cloning of 'Dolly' the sheep in 1997, with the money needed to finance the company being provided by Mark Hunt. Based in the Bahamas, the government insisted that its laboratories be closed. Immediately, another company under the same name of Clonaid was formed by Brigitte Boisselier. According to Raël, he has no control over the current company. For security reasons, the location of the company is currently being kept secret.

Why was the company formed? Three reasons can be identified. One reason is market demand or, to put it more kindly, the intention of helping married or gay couples. The latter, for example, may want a child who is a genetic replica of one of the partners.

For a heterosexual couple, perhaps it is the death of their child or a desire to take precautionary measures in case their child dies young or unexpectedly. The precaution would be to preserve samples of cells belonging to a child still living so that they could be used for organ repair or cloning in the future, if necessary.

Or it may be couples struggling with fertility problems and longing for their own child. For such people, the prospect of cloning can be attractive. They may choose to use Clonaid in an attempt to realize their dreams.

A second reason for forming this company must be financial. After all, Clonaid is a commercial company. When Clonaid began, it charged $50,000 (£35,000) for sampling and storing human cells, in a service known as Insuraclone.[2]

According to Clonaid, over one million customers worldwide are expected to be interested in Clonaid in the near future for purposes of cloning.[3] And the profit element for Clonaid can be considerable even on the 2002 cost of $200,000 (£140,000) for each future clone.

For a fee, there are other ways in which Clonaid is prepared to help people. For an infertile woman, for instance, the company offers eggs from other females for $5000 plus a significant transplantation charge. Clonaid also intends to clone pets of wealthy persons who want their dead pets brought back to life. The same service will be offered to racehorse owners. Here then is a lucrative commercial venture.

However, there is disappointment for Clonaid and their potential customers. Recent research by US scientists on cloned pigs reveals that the young produced by cloning differ significantly in appearance and behaviour 'just as much as (and sometimes more than) those produced by normal reproduction'.[4] Attempts, therefore, to replace favourite pets or replicate other animals appear doomed to failure; there may be serious implications for therapeutic cloning of human embryonic stem cells in order to create 'spare part' tissue for medical treatment.

Thirdly, it must be understood that Clonaid and the Raelian sect are driven by a philosophy and world view diametrically opposed to the Bible. Their message is unmistakable. The only prospect of living after death is by means of cloning. And it is a viable option because they believe that each person has a genetic code capable of 'technological reincarnation'.[5]

For Raël, 'cloning will enable mankind to reach eternal life. The next step will be to directly clone an adult person without having to go through the growth process and to transfer memory and personality in this person. Then, we wake up after death in a brand new body just like after a good night's sleep!'[6]

Is this fact or fiction? The Clonaid company claims it is fact. But on what basis? That between 26 December 2002 and 4 February 2003 it has successfully cloned as many as five babies which have been born in different locations. A thirty-one-year-old American lady gave birth to Eve on 26 December 2002; Eve is allegedly the first cloned baby to be born. The mothers of the other cloned babies, we are informed, include a Dutch lesbian and a Saudi Arabian Muslim.

Most scientists are not impressed. The reason? Because Clonaid 'once again has failed to substantiate them with any evidence'.[7] In fact, this reputable scientific journal insists: 'But in the absence of any information about the babies and any scientific proof that they were cloned, the claims are increasingly being dismissed as a lengthy publicity stunt.' Similarly, University of Pittsburgh researchers reported in the journal *Science* (10 April 2003) that the claim by Clonaid to have produced cloned babies is 'something never verified'.[8]

That is also the view of cloning specialist Rudolph Jaenisch at the Massachusetts Institute of Technology: 'In the absence of any scientific evidence,' he writes, 'I have to believe that it's not true.'[9] These scientists are probably right. And the onus is on Clonaid to provide evidence for independent and competent verification.

3.
A major issue

Apart from Clonaid and the Raelian movement, cloning is a major issue today. In fact, many observers regard human cloning as the most vital issue facing us over the next ten years. And the subject of human cloning raises huge questions for us all — scientific, political and ethical. These questions will be identified and addressed in the next chapter but at this point we need to report on what scientists and governments are doing and saying about human cloning.

Before we proceed, however, one distinction is crucial for us to understand, namely, the distinction between *reproductive* and *therapeutic* cloning. The former deliberately endeavours to create a genetically identical human being. This is what Clonaid claims to have achieved and what some scientists want to pursue with vigour.

By contrast, therapeutic cloning is geared to medical and research work which seeks to create new tissue from cloned stem cells outside the womb. The purpose is more restricted than that for reproductive cloning. In therapeutic cloning, the cloning of human embryos is to produce stem cells to assist in treating degenerative diseases like Parkinson's, Alzheimer's and Muscular Dystrophy. By substituting new stem cells for those cells that have been lost, it is hoped that people suffering from these degenerative, and currently incurable, conditions can be helped significantly, if not healed.

What are reputable scientists saying about these two forms of cloning? Quite a lot!

One British scientist observes there is 'a race to clone the first human'.[1] And some important steps have been taken towards achieving this goal.

There was, for example, the cloning of 'Dolly' the sheep in 1997 by a group of scientists in Scotland under Professor Ian Wilmut. Dolly died young, early in 2003, and her stuffed body is now on display at the Royal Museum of Scotland in Edinburgh.

Since the cloning of Dolly in 1997, dozens of animal clones — including cows, pigs, mice, goats and a cat — have been born. But 'many are stillborn and some survive only with severe defects'.[2] However, in 2001 scientists at Advanced Cell Technology (ACT) informed the media that they had succeeded in obtaining the birth of a baby bull gaur, a wild ox from south-east Asia. This was the first clone of an animal belonging to an endangered species; it died later from an infection.

A more important milestone was 25 November 2002 when the Massachusetts company ACT again hit the headlines. It claimed to have produced a cloned human embryo. Their aim? Certainly 'not to create cloned human beings, but to develop life-saving therapies'. How did ACT do this? They report that they used the same technique that was used to clone animals — cell nuclear replacement (CNR). This was achieved by transplanting the nucleus of an adult skin cell into an unfertilized human egg. The resultant embryo grew only to the six-cell stage after one week. If stem cells are to be harvested for therapeutic use, an embryo of sixty-four cells at least is required.

Concerning reproductive cloning, Peter Saunders, General Secretary of the UK Christian Medical Fellowship (CMF) representing nearly six thousand British doctors and medical students, reports: 'Many scientists remain sceptical as to whether it is technically possible for human clones to be born.'[3]

Roger Highfield, science editor of the *Daily Telegraph,* agrees: 'No politician or credible scientist backs the idea of reproductive cloning, where the "nuclear transfer" technique developed by Prof. Ian Wilmut and colleagues to create Dolly the sheep would be used to create a genetic copy of a person.'[4]

Only a few days after the US House of Representatives voted on 31 July 2001 to ban the use of cloning technology in medical research, Italian embryologist Severino Antinori addressed the National Academy of Scientists in Washington. His message was aggressive and uncompromising. Antinori was undeterred and would employ the same techniques used to produce Dolly the sheep in his plans for reproductive human cloning. He, and a colleague, were heavily criticized by other scientists.

Politically, several countries took action to outlaw reproductive cloning. In the United Kingdom, for example, the government moved extremely quickly in November 2002. Early in 2001 the UK government had already modified the 1990 Human Fertilisation and Embryology Act in order to legalize the cloning of human embryos for research. However, implementation of the new law was delayed because of a High Court challenge by the Pro Life Alliance, which was upheld in November 2002. As a consequence of that decision, the UK was left with no law at all on cloning.

Immediately Antinori, the Italian fertility specialist, informed the world that he was setting up a reproductive cloning clinic in the UK.

Only a week and a half after Antinori's announcement the British Government introduced its *Human Reproductive Cloning Act*. Both Houses of Parliament approved this rushed legislation, which banned an embryo being placed in a woman if created without fertilization. This government legislation, though full of weaknesses and extremely difficult to police, was intended to promote therapeutic cloning but to prevent reproductive cloning.

The loopholes in this legislation are probably being exploited already. For example, it is now possible to produce cloned embryos in the UK but arrange for the implantation to be done in another country. It is encouraging that some groups of scientists, including the Christian Medical Fellowship, have requested the government to provide more adequate legislation and also, as a matter of urgency, a moratorium on all aspects of human cloning, whether for reproduction or medical research and therapeutic use.

There is no doubt about it. Cloning is one of the major issues currently facing us in the twenty-first century. It is not going to go away.

Governments are nervous about it and many have acted to ban reproductive human cloning. Many scientists urge extreme caution and some are sceptical. Christians, too, have important reasons, ethical and biblical, for opposing human cloning; but more of that in the next chapter.

4.
Cloning and the Bible

Cloning — or to be more precise, reproductive human cloning; is it right? For Christians, the question is more specific: is cloning consistent with Bible teaching? And it is a question of major importance. But why appeal to the Bible in a contemporary discussion of cloning? The reason is because the Bible is a special book.

The Bible is special because through it God reveals to us what he is like, what he has done and is still doing, as well as what he will do in the future. For example, God created the world (Genesis 1:1; John 1:3; Colossians 1:16); he continues to sustain all life (Acts 17:28); and he rules over all (Psalm 97:1; Daniel 4:35). God has also acted decisively in Jesus Christ to redeem men and women (John 3:16; Galatians 4:4-5).

Here then is an exciting fact. The Bible provides divine light on the origin, nature and destiny of humans, even creation itself. To ignore this divine book is foolishness and will result only in misery, suffering and exploitation.

Three specific Bible principles are immediately relevant to our discussion. The first is that God has made humans in his own likeness (Genesis 1:27). This means that we are unique, with each person possessing the same dignity and worth. Human life is special and needs to be safeguarded at all stages whether in the womb, infancy, youth, adulthood or old age.

Many Christians believe that a second Bible principle is pertinent to cloning, namely, that human life begins at conception (Jeremiah 1:4-5; Psalm 51:5; 139:13-16).

A third Bible principle is relevant, too. God has instituted marriage in which children can be born and nurtured by a man and a woman who love and care for each other in a life-long commitment (Genesis 2:24; 4:1; Ephesians 5:22-33).

In order to understand the application of these biblical principles to reproductive and therapeutic human cloning, we need to start at the beginning.

What is cloning? Briefly, we can say it is 'a process that makes exact replicas of genetic material'.[1] A number of stages can be identified with regard to the process of human reproductive cloning and here is an example of one such process.

At *stage 1*, the aim is to obtain 400 eggs which are female cells. These eggs are obtained from up to forty female donors. Doctors take from each donor up to fifteen eggs. *Stage 2* involves taking cells from the person who is going to be cloned. In *stage 3*, the cell nucleus containing the DNA, that is, the genetic material found in all living organisms, is removed from each egg by means of a tiny needle.

Stage 4 involves placing the DNA-free eggs in contact with the cells of the person being cloned. An electric charge is then used to create a shock in order to fuse together both sets of cells. Usually, some eggs divide to form embryos — a term used to describe the human offspring in its earliest form in the first eight weeks from conception or fusing.

Over a short period of time, *stage 5* involves several eggs being implanted in up to fifty surrogate mothers, from which nine or ten pregnancies can result. The pregnancies may end because of miscarriage or abortion when serious, often extensive, defects are discovered.

This process of human reproductive cloning is termed asexual reproduction because all the genes of the clone are derived from a body cell of just one person. By contrast, in normal sexual reproduction a child benefits from receiving an equal number of genes from each of its parents. And in this normal process, there is no need of artificial assistance to fuse the male and female cells together.

Having now defined cloning and described the process in a somewhat simplified form, we must now repeat our question: what, in the light of the Bible, is wrong with reproductive human cloning?

Consider, for example, the biblical principle that human life begins at conception. Admittedly, this is at variance with what some scientists and members of the public believe. When one considers, however, the facts surrounding conception then the biblical principle is the only viable explanation of when human life begins.

Allow me to remind you again of what happens. In conception or fertilization, the male sperm (cell) and the female egg blend together. A technical name for what is there, after fusion, is a zygote; it is a new cell, genetically complete, and includes all that is required to form us as unique individuals. John Ling reminds us that from the zygote stage, 'the only additional requirement you needed then, and indeed have done ever since then, has been nutrition'.[2] From conception, all the changes are only those of development. That is why experienced scientist Paul Daniel warns: 'The embryo is the baby in incipient stage. It has life. Any manipulation of the embryo amounts to playing with life.'[3]

Think of this first in regard to abortion. In the United States approximately one and a half million abortions are performed annually. Since the Abortion Act of 1967 was passed by the UK Parliament, over five million unborn babies have been aborted in the UK. During 2001, in England and Wales alone, over 186,000 abortions were performed; this figure represents three and a half thousand abortions per week.

Abortion usually occurs from eight weeks onwards. Even at this early stage, the baby is perfect in terms of physical form; it is living, moving, swallowing, digesting and sucking its thumb! Abortion then involves the termination of 'the life of a real, living, human being'.[4]

A similar principle relates to cloning. Not only are human embryos exploited but many of them are deliberately destroyed in the quest for both reproductive and therapeutic human cloning. Cloning humans can lead to high foetal loss.[5]

Even in the case of therapeutic cloning, it is necessary for scientists to create the embryo initially. Scientists then destroy the embryo once the nucleus or needed cells are removed. Does this not represent the killing of human life?

The purpose in therapeutic cloning is an admirable one, possibly replacing a kidney or skin tissue in a sick patient. In the near future, it is hoped that the process can be used successfully to replace, for example, the damaged, diseased cells of patients suffering from Alzheimer's, Parkinson's or diabetes.

Christians, with others, welcome the prospect of overcoming degenerative diseases like those mentioned above, but must it be at the cost of killing the embryo once the needed cells have been removed?

Christian medical doctors prefer an alternative way and point to the recently developed research with regard to adult stem cells.

Peter Saunders reports that these have 'already been used success-fully in humans in the treatment of bowel, skin and heart disease and in other mammals for a much broader range of illnesses'.[6]

What this means is that therapeutic treatment can be given to patients without using and destroying human embryos. That is ex-cellent news. For Saunders, the evidence is 'good' and 'growing all the time, that adult human cells may be a simpler alternative to using embryonic stem cells without the practical and ethical prob-lems inherent in the cloning of human embryos'.[7] There are other major advantages, too. For example, in treating diseases like leu-kaemia, scientists have considerable experience in obtaining adult blood stem cells as well as purifying and transplanting them.

It is time to underline our three Bible principles.

1. Human life begins at conception. If you question this biblical principle then consider the statement in the Old Testament about the prophet Jeremiah: 'Before I formed you in the womb I knew you; before you were born I sanctified [lit: "set you apart"] you; and I ordained you a prophet...' (Jeremiah 1:5). One cannot es-cape the conclusion that the embryo in the womb is a person; it is known to God even before conception and God as Creator is the one who 'formed' the child. And for that child, as for Jeremiah, God has a purpose. By contrast, cloning procedures assume that embryos can be destroyed once they have served their usefulness. A growing number of Christians are persuaded that the destruction of embryos in this way also violates God's command to us not to kill (Exodus 20:13).

2. Then there is the biblical principle that humans, even in the womb, are made in the image of God; consequently, each human

has worth and dignity. God places great value on us and the ultimate proof of this is that Jesus Christ, the Son of God, assumed our
humanity and came to die for our sins on the cross.

Although this worth applies to the individual from conception,
yet the fact is ignored in cloning procedures. According to David
Gushee, cloning 'constitutes unethical experimentation on a non-
consenting human subject'.[8] That is correct. Again, people can be
cloned merely to obtain 'spare parts', so embryos are treated as a
means to an end, a commodity rather than an individual. Commercialization and exploitation will be possible especially in collect-
ing embryos which are not needed but kept in freezer storage. In its
July 2002 report on cloning, the USA President's Council on
Bioethics expressed its worry that cloning would further increase
the trend to commercialization and industrialization of human reproduction. Ling is correct in observing that the ethics of human
cloning 'tend to be totally utilitarian and utterly self-serving'.[9]

3. There is also the biblical principle that God instituted marriage
for a man and woman; in that loving, intimate relationship, God
intends that children should be conceived and born. Here is another foundational principle. Children are a heritage of the Lord
(Psalm 127:3) and it is the Lord who opens the womb. This is the
Lord's infinitely wise and gracious provision in ordaining children
as the fruit of a loving, marriage relationship (Ephesians 6:1-4;
Colossians 3:20-21). For the first time in history, it is now possible
through cloning to bring a new human into the world by using the
genetic material of one person rather than two as God intended in
marriage. In cloning procedures, there is no essential difference
between cell fusion methods mentioned earlier in the chapter and
CNR, which is cell nuclear replacement. Although using different

methods, both involve the introduction of a cell nucleus into a de-nucleated cell. Male sperm is not required in either procedure. Describing the CNR method of cloning, John Ling writes: 'The nucleus, which contains the genetic material, is removed from a body cell, perhaps a skin or liver cell, taken from the animal, or perhaps in the near future, the human patient, to be cloned. This nucleus is then transferred, as a replacement, into a donated ovum, from the same species, which is non-nucleated... Again, culturing, reprogramming and stimulation are required to produce an embryonic clone ... sperm is not needed in CNR...'[10] The implications for the role of men in human reproduction could be profound and frightening.

Peter Saunders sums up the biblical principle well: 'God ordained that his image in human beings (Genesis 1:27) was to be passed on in the context of a loving committed marriage relationship, through sexual union (Genesis 2:24) and that children should be reared, protected, disciplined and educated within the context of a stable family relationship. We disregard his wisdom at our peril.'[11]

There are further objections to cloning which it is not possible to discuss here, such as the potential emotional damage to the child and the possible loss of their sense of individuality. Considerable tension could also exist in family relations in terms of multiple generations within the same family, as well as in broken relations such as divorce.

One thing is clear. Clonaid intends to press on with reproductive human cloning, whatever the Bible says. And the main reason for doing so will be discussed briefly in the next chapter.

5.
Raelians and eternal life

It is 'the first company in the world to offer a human cloning service'. That is Clonaid's claim. But why do they emphasize cloning? Some reasons were suggested earlier but one reason is extremely important to Clonaid and Raelians.

That reason is expressed by Raël in confident terms: 'cloning will enable mankind to reach eternal life'.[1] It is a bold but wild claim, made in the context of some bizarre ideas and beliefs.

December 1973 is a significant date. According to Raël, he was driving to work in the French town of Clermont-Ferrand. On a sudden impulse, instead of driving to his office, he turned in the direction of a local volcano site.

At this point, the story becomes fantasy. Raël claims that an extraterrestrial being came out of a flying saucer and approached him at the site. The visitor informed Raël that humans had been created through a complicated cloning procedure by people called 'Elohim' who came from a different planet.

The fantasy continues. Raël asks us to believe he was transported to the planet where these Elohim live. They then appointed him as their messenger to inform humans on earth of their true origins and identity.

What is this message? Rejecting Christianity with great vehemence, Raël teaches that about 25,000 years ago, extra-terrestrial beings called Elohim created all the varied forms of life which exist. Use of the Bible name 'Elohim' for these creatures is irresponsible. Concerning Raël's translation of the Hebrew word as 'those who came from the sky', the name is the most frequently used name for God in the Old Testament. The word is also applied on occasions to the gods of other nations as well as to humans, especially those serving as judges. In Hebrew, the word is in the plural but this is a plural of majesty highlighting the greatness and splendour of the one, eternal, living God. It also includes a reference to the Trinity of divine persons within the Godhead — Father, Son and Holy Spirit. What is certain is that the name does not refer in any way to extraterrestrial creatures.

According to Raël these beings used their advanced knowledge of genetics and cell biology to create all the varied forms of life that exist. They used chemicals and their own selected DNA to create these life forms, working in laboratories in an area now recognized as Israel. Humans are the result of their work, according to Raël, and they were created in the image of the Elohim.

Cloning, then, for Raël is the only path to immortality because humans have no soul. What they have is a genetic code with potential for technological reincarnation. After death, 'there is nothing', they tell us, not even heaven or reincarnation. Cloning alone is the key.

According to Raël the Elohim intend to return in A.D. 2025 to Jerusalem. Prior to this, a multimillion-dollar embassy and landing area must be completed there, otherwise the Elohim will not return! What will happen then? Raelianism will become the dominant world religion and followers could be taken to the planet inhabited by the Elohim.

What about here and now? Raelians want adults, particularly older folk, to be cloned. This cloning is intended to include the transfer of memories and personality into bodies which are younger and healthier but real lookalikes. Here is 'the ultimate eschatological experiment'.[2] It is the only way, they insist, to unending life on earth.

Fantasy? Yes, most certainly. To anticipate the prospect of uninhibited freedom and enjoyment to pursue sin, sensuality, ecstasy, sex, and to imagine they can do so permanently on earth, is sheer fantasy.

The reality is totally different: 'it is appointed for men to die once', God's Word declares, 'but after this the judgement' (Hebrews 9:27). There is no escape from physical death, not even by cloning. And the reality is that all humans have a soul or spiritual dimension which survives death — permanently.

Now that is a fact and the Lord Jesus Christ confirmed this on many occasions.

Consider the story, for example, he related concerning two men who died. The men were very different. One was rich and lived luxuriously, but he was not a believer. He had no time for God; he only wanted to enjoy himself.

The other man, Lazarus, was desperately poor but happy. He trusted and loved God; he also knew his sins were forgiven. That was the key to his happiness. He knew he would live for ever in heaven.

Eventually both men died; yes, both survived death, as we all will. Lazarus, the believer, went to heaven. His happiness was complete for heaven is a fantastic place. Only believers, however, can go there.

Tragically, the fate of the other man was different. He died and went immediately to hell, a place of unimaginable suffering and agony where all unbelievers go when they die (Luke 16:23-28).

Concerned? Do you want genuine eternal life? The next chapter can help you.

6.
Fantasy?

Fantasy! It is an appropriate word to describe Raelian beliefs. Their teachings that humans were created by extra-terrestrial beings 25,000 years ago or that these aliens have a home planet less than one light year away are sheer fantasy. They have no supporting evidence and science actually informs us that the nearest star system is over four light years away.

By contrast, Christianity is based on solid historical evidence; it is certainly not fantasy. To illustrate the point, I want to refer to the Bible and first to 2 Peter 1:16-18.

The writer here is exposing the ideas of false teachers but also reminding Christians of major Christian teachings, especially the return of the Lord Jesus Christ to this world. Only God knows when this will occur. But Christ will return personally, visibly and in glory to usher in the end of the world.

Fantasy? Certainly not, and Peter, the writer, comes straight to the point in verse 16. He insists: 'We did not follow cunningly devised fables' or myths in teaching about Christ's coming. On what basis can he make this claim? His first answer is in verses 16-18 and it is a powerful one. Peter refers to an incident in the life of

Jesus Christ on earth which is known as the transfiguration (Matthew 17:1-8; Mark 9:2-8; Luke 9:28-36).

Fantasy? Not at all because there are two lines of evidence. First, unlike Raël, a group of these men rather than a single individual witnessed the incident. Secondly, they saw (v. 16) and heard (v. 18) remarkable things with regard to Jesus.

Think of the eyewitness aspect to begin with. These men were 'eyewitnesses of his majesty' (v. 16). What they saw was not small extra-terrestrial beings with long black hair, small black beards and green suits, as Raël claimed. It was infinitely more glorious. Jesus Christ was none other than God manifested in the flesh. Suddenly, his deity shone with brilliance through his clothes. His face shone like the sun (Matthew 17:2) and his clothes sparkled in dazzling white (Mark 9:3). The sight was breathtaking.

However, there is more: 'We heard this voice which came from heaven...' (v. 18). It was a divine, heavenly voice, not a human one. The message from heaven is emphatic and uncompromising: 'This is my beloved Son...' These words point to a unique relation of Jesus to God the Father; he is the eternal Son, greatly loved by the Father, 'in whom', he adds, 'I am well pleased'. Pause a moment and consider this crucial point.

Jesus was more than a mere human. He was both God and man. His home was heaven. That was where he had come from: 'I have come down from heaven...', he insisted (John 6:38). And in heaven he was worshipped, served and obeyed by angels and believers. In fact, he was equal to the Father and Holy Spirit.

No wonder the voice from heaven said, 'This is my beloved Son'; his eternal relation to God the Father was one of equality, love and delight. He enjoyed the most intimate relationship with his Father (John 1:18).

Why then did he leave heaven? This question brings us to the heart of Christianity. He came to this world on a unique rescue mission. But the mission was planned and executed by God himself; prompted by his free, amazing love. 'For God so loved the world that he gave his only begotten Son, that whoever believes in him should not perish but have everlasting life' (John 3:16).

Because he was God, assuming our human nature involved a miraculous conception in the womb of the virgin Mary about 2000 years ago (Luke 1:35). This happened in history. He was 'Immanuel', meaning 'God with us' (Matthew 1:23). And what he tells us about the Father, heaven, forgiveness or eternal life must be true because he is God. The many amazing miracles he performed in his ministry also confirmed that he is God. This is firm historical evidence. At the transfiguration, three disciples caught a glimpse of Christ's divine glory. Some of his disciples were also present at his death on the cross and, along with hundreds of other people, witnessed Jesus' resurrection from the dead. In 1 Corinthians 15:5-8, Paul marshals the historical evidence for Jesus' resurrection by referring to various individuals and groups who saw him alive. This event is historically attested.

What was Jesus like? Certainly very different from Raël. According to Raël, we are 'born for pleasure'[1] and the key to societal transformation is the personal development of sensuality.[2] By contrast, Jesus was morally perfect; he never thought or said or did anything which violated God's laws (1 Peter 2:22-24).

That is marvellous news. All humans, not just Raël, have sinned (Romans 3:23) and are under the sentence of eternal death (Romans 6:23), but Jesus actively and completely fulfilled the law in his life but on our behalf.

How did he rescue us? The climax was his unique death on the cross where he 'suffered once for sins, the just for the unjust, that he might bring us to God' (1 Peter 3:18). This means that all the punishment due to us because of our sins was taken voluntarily by Jesus Christ as our substitute.

Is eternal life possible? Yes, it is. Who gives it? Only God; no man, organization or even church can give it. No cloning either will secure eternal life. Even if it was possible to clone a human being and to pass on all the memories, the 'cloner' would still die, and with death the soul of the individual will either go to heaven or to hell. There is never any indication that soul and memories are the same. We are more than a collection of chemicals, no matter how complex.

What must I do to receive eternal life? Only believe in the Lord Jesus Christ: 'whoever believes in him should not perish but have eternal life' (John 3:16). Is it free? Completely free; 'the gift of God is eternal life in Christ Jesus our Lord' (Romans 6:23). No clone can ever provide eternal life.

And that is not the end either. Because all humans are in the grip of sin (John 8:34) and spiritual death (Ephesians 2:1), no one can go unaided to Christ and believe. For this reason, God works a miracle of new birth within us (John 3:3, 5, 7); it is a supernatural, radical work which changes us inwardly and imparts spiritual life to us. In the exercise of that new life, we are given grace to believe on the Lord Jesus and receive the precious gift of eternal life and forgiveness.

There is more, too! God stays with the believer through all the circumstances of life and he guarantees that each believer at death enters into heaven (Romans 8:31-39; 1 Peter 1:3-5).

Even that is not the end! The one who was transfigured, who died, rose from the dead and ascended will return in glory. Our dead bodies will then be raised and conformed to the glorious body of Christ (Philippians 3:21). This, not human cloning, is the hope of the Christian because when he appears, 'we shall be like him, for we shall see him as he is' (1 John 3:2). There will even be 'new heavens and a new earth in which righteousness dwells' (2 Peter 3:13).

But it all begins here and exclusively so: 'And this is eternal life, that they may know you, the only true God, and Jesus Christ whom you have sent' (John 17:3).

Notes

Chapter 2
1. Raël Press File, *Founder of Clonaid,* undated.
2. See 'Raël creates the first human cloning company', 10 March 1997 press release.
3. Clonaid com: *The First Human Cloning Company,* p.2.
4. *Evangelical Times,* June 2003, p.2.
5. See Raël's *Let's Welcome Our Fathers,* p.44.
6. Raël Press File, *Founder Of Clonaid,* undated.
7. NewScientist.com, 'Special Report: Cloning and Stem Cells', p.1.
8. CNN.com/Health.
9. As above.

Chapter 3
1. *Human Cloning,* Paul P. Daniel, p.21, Mall Publishing, Niles.
2. CNAA.com/Health 10.4.03 'Study: Obstacles Prevent Human Cloning', p.1.
3. *Triple Helix,* Winter 2002, 'Cloning — the Latest Developments,' p.4.
4. *Daily Telegraph,* 23 April 2003, p.18.

Chapter 4
1. www.bioethics.net, 'Human Cloning: is it moral?', p.1, Winter 2002.

2. *Responding to the Culture of Death: A Primer of Bioethical Issues*, p.25, Day One Publications 2001.
3. Daniel, *Human Cloning*, p.10.
4. *Ibid.*, p.31.
5. *Triple Helix*, p.2.
6. www.cmf.org.uk/helix/win02/cloning.htm
7. www.cmf.org.uk/nucleus/nucapr01/cloning.htm
8. www.baptiststandard.com/2003/comment_gushee.html
9. Ling, *Culture of Death*, p.43.
10. *Ibid.*, p.42.
11. www.cmf.org.uk/helix/win02/cloning.htm

Chapter 5

1. www.rael.org/int/press_site/english/pages/clonaid.htm.
2. *Yes to Human Cloning*, pp.36-37, 101-112, Raël.

Chapter 6

1. *Yes to Human Cloning*, p.11, c.v. Raël.
2. *Let's Welcome Our Fathers*, pp.64-65, c.v. Raël; also, *The True Face of God*, p.175, c.v. Raël.

If you need further help, please contact the following: